Schooner Sultana - 1768
Colonial History Curriculum Unit

Table of Contents

1

 Brainstorming Activity: KWL Chart

NAME: _____ **DATE:** _____

Directions: Use the KWL Chart to brainstorm things you already know about Sultana and what you would like to find out. After you have finished learning about Sultana in class and have visited the ship, fill in the **L** column which indicates what you learned about the vessel and colonial history.

K What Do I Know About The Subject?	**W** What Do I Want To Find Out?	**L** What Have I Learned?

Activity #1 — Life Before Electricity

When Sultana was under sail from 1768 to 1773, electricity had yet to be discovered. Have each of your students make a list of modern appliances which use electricity. When their lists are complete, make a master list on the blackboard which incorporates input from as many different students as possible. Discuss the fact that in Sultana's time none of the items on the list would have existed. How would your students' lives had been different had they lived in the 18th century? How would they entertain themselves without radios, CD players, televisions, or computers? What would they do without air conditioning, heat, or electrical lighting in their homes? How would they contact friends in distant neighborhoods without phones? This activity helps students realize how many modern conveniences we take for granted and clearly illuminates differences between life in modern society versus life in colonial times.

Activity #2 — Travel

Another invention which had not yet arrived in colonial times was the gas powered engine. Have each student make a list of ways that people get from one place to another in today's society. How many of their methods relied on gas powered machines? Discuss means that colonists would have used to travel from one location to another. How much slower would travel have been in the 18th century? What would be the fastest way to travel over land? What would be the fastest way to travel over water? How would the lack of gas powered machines have affected colonists' commerce? How would it have affected long distance communication? This activity helps students understand the colonists' reliance on sail power and again illuminates major differences between present day and colonial society.

1768 Draught of the Schooner Sultana

Draught of Sultana recorded by Royal Navy surveyors on June 21, 1768 at Deptford Navy Yard outside Greenwich, England.
Courtesy National Maritime Museum, Greenwich, England.

Schooner Sultana — the 1768 Draught

NAME: _____ DATE: _____

Directions: Use the copy of the original draught of Sultana to answer the following questions.

1. What general information does the draught give you about the ship?

2. The draught provides three different views of Sultana. What information does each view provide?

3. Pretend you are the person in charge of building the ship. What are the steps you would need to take to get the project started? How would the draught help you plan your strategy?

Schooner Sultana — the 1768 Draught

Create a Draught for Your Own Ship

Pretend you are building a ship during the colonial era. In the space provided, create a draught of your vessel. Include a side view, a head-on view, and an overhead view of your craft. Use the original draught of Sultana as a reference.

NAME OF SHIP: _____ LENGTH ON DECK: _____

TONNAGE (weight): _____ WIDTH: _____ DEPTH: _____

SIDE VIEW

OVERHEAD VIEW

HEAD-ON VIEW

Schooner Sultana 1768:
About the Captain

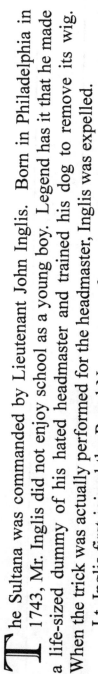

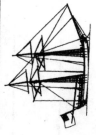

The Sultana was commanded by Lieutenant John Inglis. Born in Philadelphia in 1743, Mr. Inglis did not enjoy school as a young boy. Legend has it that he made a life-sized dummy of his hated headmaster and trained his dog to remove its wig. When the trick was actually performed for the headmaster, Inglis was expelled.

Lt. Inglis first joined the Royal Navy at age fourteen. In 1758, he was put under the command of Captain John Elliot on the H.M.S. *Hussar.* Captain Elliot would turn out to be the major influence in Inglis' naval career, serving as his teacher, advisor, and friend for the next fifty years of his life.

Inglis served on several ships in the Seven Years War, which pitted the English navy against the French and Spanish. He participated in many battles, several of which involved the capture of enemy French ships. During the Seven Years War, on October 22, 1761, Inglis was commissioned a 4th Lieutenant in the Royal Navy.

From 1768 to 1773, Inglis commanded the H.M. schooner SULTANA. During these years he and his crew boarded hundreds of colonial ships while enforcing Parliament's tax laws on the English colonists in North America. While Sultana was stationed in the Potomac River, Lieutenant Inglis was invited to dine with George Washington at Mt. Vernon.

During the Revolutionary War in 1778, Inglis was commanding the H.M. sloop *Senegal* when he was captured by several French ships of war. He was taken to court, where it was found that he acted prudently in the face of a superior force by turning his ship over to the French navy. Ironically, Inglis recaptured the *Senegal* in 1780 while battling the French off the coast of Africa. .

In the latter years of his life, Inglis was promoted to Vice Admiral, one of the highest ranking positions in the Royal Navy. He died in 1807 at the age of 63. He had served in two of the most important wars the world had ever seen, been involved in several battles and captured many ships, and served his country admirably. His legacy lives on with the reconstruction of SULTANA.

Image of John Inglis selected from The Family of Inglis of Auchindinny and Red Hall by John Alexander Inglis, Edinburgh 1914.

Schooner Sultana: Writing to Persuade
Help Lieutenant Inglis Recruit His Crew!

Directions: Imagine that you are trying to recruit crew members for the Schooner Sultana, which will be sailing from England to North America under the command of Lieutenant John Inglis. Your job is to convince twenty four people to work on board the ship. In the space below, write a promotional piece that might convince potential crew members to join the vessel's work force. Include at least three positive aspects of working on an English naval ship. Fill in the box with an illustration that might help to further persuade someone to come aboard.

illustration

PERSUASIVE ORGANIZER

Prior to writing your recruitment article, fill out this Persuasive Organizer to help structure your paragraph.

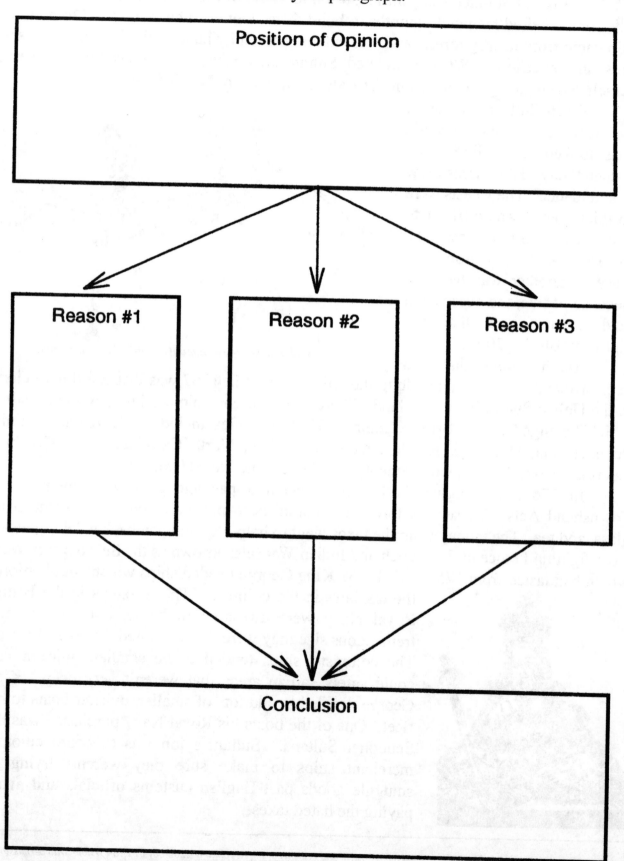

Position of Opinion

Reason #1

Reason #2

Reason #3

Conclusion

The original Sultana was built in Boston in 1767. It took a working crew of fifty to one hundred men eight months to build the schooner. The wood used to build the ship came from nearby forests and was cut and carved by hand with giant saws, chisels, axes, and other tools. When completed, Sultana was intended to be used as a merchant vessel, carrying cargo to and from ports along the coast of North America.

When Sultana was built, the land along the Atlantic coast looked very different than it does today. Huge trees grew in abundance. The forests were so thick that it was difficult to build roads. In most cases, the easiest way to get from one place to another was by boat. Because of this, the oceans and tidal rivers were like the highways of the 1700's.

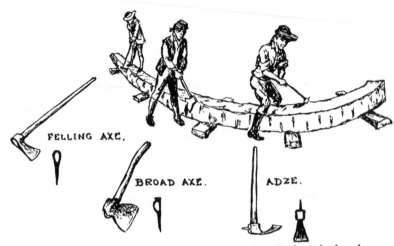

Men in a colonial shipyard shaping a "rib" of a boat by hand.

Another thing that was very different about the land along the Atlantic coast in 1767 was that it did not belong to the United States, but to England. There were thirteen colonies hugging the coastline which belonged to the British empire. These colonies included Maryland, Virginia, Pennsylvania, Delaware, Rhode Island, New York, North Carolina, South Carolina, Georgia, Massachusetts, Connecticut, New Jersey, and New Hampshire.

In 1767, the English Parliament enacted a package of laws known as the Townshend Acts. These acts forced the colonists to pay taxes on paper, paint, lead, glass, and tea. The money from the taxes went to help England pay back a debt they had from fighting France in the French and Indian War (also known as the Seven Years War), which had lasted from 1755 until 1763. King George needed ships which could enforce

the tax laws in the colonies. The warships in the British Royal Navy were awesome in battle, but due to their tremendous size they weren't well suited for coastal patrol. The colonists' ships tended to be smaller, quicker, and could safely sail in areas that weren't very deep. King George decided to add lots of smaller, quicker boats to his fleet. One of the boats his Royal Navy purchased was the Schooner Sultana. Sultana's job was to board colonial merchant ships to make sure they weren't trying to smuggle goods past English customs officials and avoid paying the hated taxes.

Image of men in a colonial shipyard reprinted from Pirates and Patriots of the Revolution ©2000 by C. Keith Wilbur with permission from The Globe Pequot Press, Guilford, CT, 1-800-962-0973, www.globe-pequot.com.

Sultana patrolled the coast of America from 1768 through 1772. During this time, her crew members searched over 800 boats. Often times colonial sailors resented having their ships searched, which made Sultana's job very dangerous. The crew often had to board colonial ships with their muskets loaded and their swivel guns aimed at the

other ship's crew. Swivel guns were like small cannons which were loaded with lead balls (grape shot) or hundreds of small pieces of metal (shrapnel) instead of a cannonball. They were used to shoot people and tear up other boats' sails and rigging. When the colonial merchants saw that Sultana's crew was willing to fight, they would usually let them board their ships.

The most dangerous event Sultana was involved with occurred off the coast of Rhode Island on January 21, 1771. While searching a small sloop in Newport Harbor, Lieutenant Inglis spotted a man on board named Thomas Roberts, who had deserted Sultana two months earlier. Inglis immediately ordered the man to be seized. Later that evening, a group of irate colonists rowed out in small boats and surrounded Sultana, threatening to cut the anchor line and set fire to the schooner. After several tense moments, Lieutenant Inglis and his crew barely managed to escape from the harbor without being captured and sunk!

Ultimately the Royal Navy decided that Sultana was too small to be of use in North America. Her size put her at a disadvantage during armed conflicts with colonial vessels. The tiny schooner was also ill-suited for the pounding she received during rough Atlantic winters. Furthermore, the schooner had failed to generate any significant amount of revenue for England. In August, 1772, Sultana was sailed back to England. Several months after her arrival, she was sold into private service for the sum of 85 British pounds.

Two years after the sale of Sultana, England and the colonies went to war against each other. The conflict was called the Revolutionary War. It lasted eight long years and ended when the English surrendered to George Washington's army at Yorktown. Finally the colonists no longer had to pay the King's taxes that Sultana had helped to enforce several years earlier.

Map of the Chesapeake Bay, 1768. Sultana spent one year in the Bay patrolling the Hampton Roads area and the mouth of the Potomac River.

Schooner Sultana: the History
Comprehension Questions

Name: _____ Date: _____

DIRECTIONS: Use information from the reading to complete .

1. How were ship building techniques used to construct Sultana different from techniques shipbuilders would use today?

_____

_____

_____

2. How has the nature of the land along the Atlantic coast changed over the years? What activities have people engaged in that led to these changes?

_____

_____

_____

3. In your opinion, what did England stand to gain from establishing colonies on the Atlantic coast?

_____

_____

_____

4. How did the French and Indian War lead to the taxation of the colonies by King George III?

_____

_____

_____

_____

5. Pretend you are a colonial merchant sailing along the Atlantic coast. Out of nowhere, the Sultana appears and orders you to come about. You must stand by helplessly as Sultana's crew members rummage through your cargo. The search takes hours and completely throws off your schedule. In the space below, describe how you feel while this is taking place.

_____

_____

_____

_____

_____

_____

6. In your opinion, how did the tax laws enacted by the English Parliament lead to the Revolutionary War? What role, if any, did Sultana play in angering the colonists to the point of warfare?

_____

_____

_____

_____

7. How was Sultana's small size problematic in enabling the ship to perform her duty?

_____

_____

_____

_____

Writing Activity

A daily activity for the captain and sail master was to write entries in the ship log, often at the beginning or end of a work day. Have your students imagine that they work and live on Sultana. Use the Student Ship Log provided (you will need to make copies) to have them write journal entries that describe the events of two days at sea. They could choose to write about Sultana's activities in the Chesapeake Bay, the gun fight in Rhode Island, or sailing across the Atlantic from England when the ship was caught in heavy seas. Other topics might include boarding a colonial merchant ship, punishing a crew member for inappropriate behavior, or going into a colonial town to buy food and supplies.

If your students are strong writers and need more space simply copy the cover of the log, fold it, and leave the inside blank. For an added challenge have the students write continuous journal entries that cover an extended period of time.

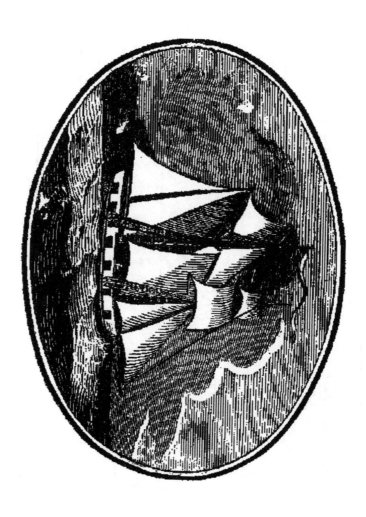

Schooner Sultana
1768

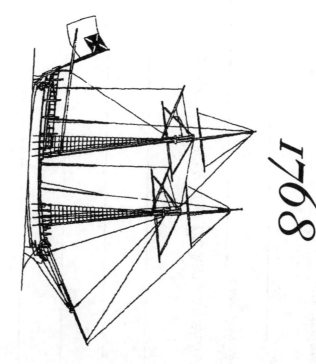

Student Ship
Log

Schooner Sultana Ship Log

Name of Sailor: _____

Month and Year _____

Date: _____

Location of Ship: _____

COMMENTS ON BOARD H.M. SCHOONER SULTANA:

_____

_____

_____

_____

_____

_____

_____

_____

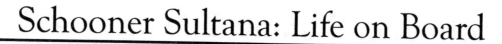

Life on Sultana was hard. The boat was crowded, the food was often moldy or rotten, and even the water could be unsafe for drinking. Sanitation was poor, and the work was very stressful and dangerous. Despite these conditions, service in the Royal Navy often provided members of the working class with their best opportunity for employment.

Sultana had a working crew of twenty five men. Crew members came from all over the world. One man who worked on Sultana, Prince Gould, was a free black man from Rhode Island. Other men came from England, Ireland, Wales, Scotland, Bermuda, Guinea, Canada, Scotland, Prussia, Norway and Sweden. Some crew members were born in the thirteen colonies. At least fifteen others were forced to work on the schooner against their will. This was called being "pressed" into service, a practice used by captains when they couldn't find enough crew members to properly run the ship.

A typical able bodied seamen in the British Royal Navy. Image courtesy of Marcy Dunn Ramsey.

The captain, surgeon and master had luxurious living quarters compared to the rest of the crew. While these three men slept in their own rooms in the rear half of the boat, the other twenty two men had to share the other half! They slept down below deck in bunk beds that were built into the sides of the ship above the food and cargo. The men only had three to four feet of space between the ceiling and the planked "floor" on top of the food casks, so they literally had to crawl into bed. There were only thirteen bunks for twenty five people, so crew members slept in shifts called watches.

The sailors' diet consisted of very few different kinds of food. They survived mainly on beef, pork, bread, peas, and fish. One kind of bread the men ate was hard tack, a circular biscuit that was dehydrated to keep mold away. Since the bread was stored in a moist, damp space it often

~HARD TACK~
MIX ONE TEASPOON OF SALT WITH ONE POUND OF FLOUR.
SHIP ENOUGH WATER TO MAKE A VERY STIFF DOUGH.
CUT THE WHOLE INTO FOUR INCH SECTIONS AND PUNCH IT WITH HOLES.
BAKE IN A FLAT PAN AT 250° FOR TWO OR THREE HOURS.

Hard tack was often hard as wood and needed to be broken with a hammer.

Image of hard tack reprinted from <u>Pirates and Patriots of the Revolution</u> ©2000 by C. Keith Wilbur with permission from The Globe Pequot Press, Guilford, CT, 1-800-962-0973, www.globe-pequot.com.

became moldy, infested with bugs, and unfit to eat. Often times the men ate the bread anyway, insects and all. The meats needed to be dried and salted so that they wouldn't rot. Usually meat was boiled and eaten as stew. A major problem that was common on 18th century ships was the presence of rats. Rats often would eat through the wooden barrels to get to the sailors' food supplies, so they lined important storage areas with lead to keep them out.

Keeping rats out of the food was a challenge for many 18th century ships, including Sultana.

If a crew member misbehaved on Sultana, punishment was swift and severe. A typical punishment was to get twelve lashes with a whip on the bare back. The most common behavior the men were punished for was drunkenness. This was because Sultana carried large amounts of beer and rum. These drinks were popular on Royal Navy ships in the 1700's because they were able to stay fresh for extended periods at sea due to the preservative effects of alcohol. Drinking large quantities of alcohol also helped sailors temporarily escape the harsh reality of their lives on board.

Every day on Sultana was filled with hard work. Jobs on board included cleaning the decks, hoisting the sails, lowering the sails, raising the anchor, lowering the anchor, adjusting the rigging, coiling ropes, spinning yarn, untangling lines, loading food, unloading food, and clearing deck space. Sometimes the captain would purposely run the Sultana into the beach so the men could scrape the bottom while the ship was tipped over. At other times men would be ordered to shore to collect firewood, find water, buy food, or get important items from town. Many crew members who were sent to run errands on shore ran away and never came back. These men were called deserters. Fifty nine men deserted Sultana between 1768 and 1772.

Sultana was probably not a place you would have wanted to work. For those who did, it was an extremely hard and demanding life.

Runaways were common on 18th century ships in the Royal Navy, which often made it difficult for captains to find enough men to properly run the ship.

Name: _____ Date: _____

1. Pretend you are a crew member working on Sultana. Use the space below to describe a typical day and night on board. Include descriptions of the work you are assigned to do, a meal you ate, and your sleeping arrangements. Describe the sights, smells, and sounds you experience at sea.

_____

_____

_____

_____

_____

_____

_____

_____

2. LIST the countries Sultana's crew members came from.

A._____   G _____

B._____   H. _____

C._____   I. _____

D _____   J. _____

E._____   K. _____

F. _____   L. _____

Use a map of the world in your classroom to find each of these countries.

3. You have chosen to work on Sultana. Since it is a relatively small boat that will be shared by twenty five people, all of the personal items you bring on board must fit into a small belongings chest. In the space below, tell what items you would choose to bring with you. Explain why you chose each item.

_____

_____

_____

_____

_____

_____

_____

4. When a man was whipped for misbehavior on Sultana, why do you think Captain Inglis had the rest of the crew watch what was happening?

_____

_____

_____

5. Would you have wanted to work on Sultana? Why or why not?

_____

_____

_____

_____

INTRODUCTION

Hard tack was an important part of a sailor's diet on ships in the 18th century. Hard tack was a small biscuit of bread made from flour, water, and butter or oil. It was a good food product to have on ships because once the bread hardened and dried it could last for a long time without spoiling. Since sailors were often at sea for months at a time, they needed foods which wouldn't rot.

Today you will make a batch of hard tack with your class. Perhaps you will be brave enough to try one of these biscuits once they have been cooked.

PREPARING THE BATCH OF BREAD

Groups of four to six students.

To make hard tack, your group will need the following materials from the Materials Center prepared by your teacher:

- One pound of flour
- One teaspoon of salt
- Enough water to make a very stiff dough (the exact amount will be determined by your teacher)
- One large mixing bowl
- One large spoon or other utensil to use for mixing the flour and water
- One stick of butter
- A flat pan
- A ruler

Follow these directions to get your batch of hard tack ready for the oven:

1. Pour the flour into the mixing bowl.
2. Mix in one teaspoon of salt.
3. Pour the water into the bowl. Mix the contents into a stiff dough using your large spoon.
4. Spread butter onto your flat pan.
5. Shape the dough by hand into small circular biscuits which are 4 inches in diameter. Use your ruler to measure the size of each biscuit
6. Place the biscuits on the flat pan until all the dough has been used.
7. Bake in an oven at 250 degrees for two to three hours.

Once the batch is completed, you will have a first-hand look at one of the food items that was eaten by Sultana's crew in the 1700's!

Goods such as tobacco, rum, and molasses were packaged in large barrels called hogsheads.

Commerce in Maryland in the 1700's was conducted over water. Due to the fact that adequate road systems had yet to be developed, the quickest and easiest way to send large quantities of goods from one location to another was by boat. Major cities such as Annapolis, Baltimore, and Norfolk developed along the water's edge. Wooden sailing ships connected these cities to the rest of the world.

In the 18th century economy, goods such as rum, sugar, molasses, salt, raisins, and spices were transported by boat from islands in the Caribbean to Maryland and other colonies. These items were called imports. A wide variety of items such as candles, wine, cloth, soap, glass, boat supplies, and tea were imported from England and other countries in Western Europe. After these ships unloaded their supplies, they often received important items from the colonists to send back to countries in Western Europe. Goods which were sent from Maryland to ports overseas were called exports. Some of the major goods exported from Maryland were grain, tobacco, corn, and lumber.

Farming was extremely important to the colonial economy of Maryland. As farms grew in size, so did the demand for cheap labor. One of the most important items shipped to Maryland from overseas was the indentured servant. Indentured servants were individuals who agreed to work on a land owner's plantation in exchange for a paid trip across the ocean. After four years, indentured servants were free to practice their trade independently. Other laborers imported to Maryland were slaves. Most slaves came from Africa. They were forced to work in the fields tilling, weeding, planting, and harvesting crops. Slaves were considered the property of the master and were often bought and sold at auction, splitting up entire families. Slaves remained an important source of labor for Maryland's economy until the 1860's.

Shipping was the major way of transporting goods in Maryland's economy until roads were improved and the railroad was invented in the 1800's. Even with the invention of railroads and automobiles, shipping remains an important element of Maryland's economy today.

Smaller vessels such as sloops and schooners were commonly used on the Chesapeake Bay for transporting goods to other colonial ports.

1. Why was shipping the easiest way to transport goods in the 1700's?

_____

_____

_____

2. What were some goods imported to Maryland in the 1700's? Where did these items come from?

_____

_____

_____

_____

3. What were some goods which were exported from Maryland in the 1700's? Where were these items sent?

_____

_____

_____

_____

4. What were some differences between slaves and indentured servants?

_____

_____

_____

_____

_____

_____

_____

Navigation: Latitude and Longitude

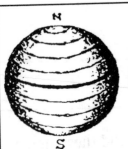

Latitude lines run horizontally across the globe and are used to measure distances north and south of the equator.

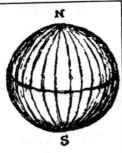

Longitude lines run vertically across the globe and are used to measure distances east and west of Greenwich, England.

Figuring out the location of the ship without the benefit of today's technology was a huge challenge for 18th century sailors. To locate their position on a map, navigators determined their latitude and longitude.

Look at a globe in your classroom. If you look carefully, you will notice a series of parallel lines running horizontally around the globe. These are called latitude lines.

The horizontal line which runs around the center of the earth is called the equator. Half of the latitude lines run from the equator to the top of the globe. These lines measure distances north of the equator. The lines which run towards the bottom of the globe measure distances south of the equator.

Another set of lines run vertically around the globe. These are called longitude lines. They are used to measure distances traveled east and west from a fixed point on the earth. The fixed point from which longitude lines are measured is Greenwich, England.

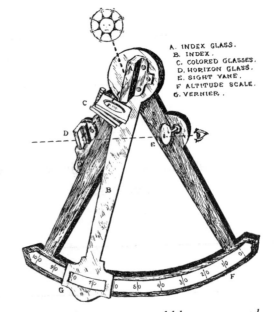

A. INDEX GLASS.
B. INDEX.
C. COLORED GLASSES.
D. HORIZON GLASS.
E. SIGHT VANE.
F. ALTITUDE SCALE.
G. VERNIER.

The arm of the sextant would be maneuvered until the sun's reflection lined up with the navigator's line of sight with the horizon, creating an angle that was measured at the bottom of the device.

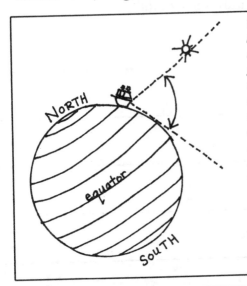

The angle created by the noon sun, the ship, and the visible horizon gave navigators a reading they could convert to degrees latitude by using a chart in the Nautical Almanac. Envision how this angle would change as the ship traveled further north or south.

If a navigator knew his latitude and longitude, he could figure out precisely where his ship was positioned. To find the ship's latitude, sailors used a tool called a sextant. The sextant measured the angle created by the noon sun, the ship, and the visible horizon. When the measurement of this angle was determined, it could be converted to degrees latitude by using a chart provided in the Nautical Almanac.

Latitude and Longitude

While navigators could figure out their latitude with sufficient accuracy, calculating the ship's longitudinal position was a much more difficult task. One way longitude was determined was by telling time. If a captain had a timepiece set to Greenwich time, he could compare that time to the time on board. For every four minutes the clocks differed, the ship had traveled one degree of longitude east or west. There was one problem with using this method during the years which Sultana sailed the Atlantic Coast: no clock had been developed yet which kept completely accurate time at sea. If the clock was off by only a few minutes per week, it would throw the navigator's calculations off by hundreds of miles!

What did navigators do about this problem? One solution was to sail well to one side of the desired location, then set a course due east or west once the necessary latitude had been reached. Another solution was called ded reckoning. In this technique, navigators would keep track of the ship's speed every hour or two, then calculate the distance they had traveled over the course of the day. If one knew the latitude, course, and distance the ship had traveled, an educated guess could be made as to the ship's longitudinal position on a map or globe.

Without an accurate clock at sea, navigators had a difficult time determining the ship's longitudinal position on the globe.

Problems determining longitude led to many lost vessels and a good number of shipwrecks. The longitude problem would plague sailors for many years to come until an accurate timepiece called a chronometer was perfected after the Revolutionary War.

Navigation: Comprehension Questions

Name: _____ Date: _____

DIRECTIONS: Answer each question in a complete sentence.

1. What do latitude lines measure?

_____

_____

2. What do longitude lines measure?

_____

_____

3. How did navigators determine their latitude?

_____

_____

4. What was the problem with using clocks to calculate longitude?

_____

_____

5. What is ded reckoning?

_____

_____

6. What invention finally solved the longitude problem?

_____

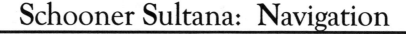
Hands-On Activity

Have Your Students Make Latitude and Longitude Lines On a Grapefruit "Globe"

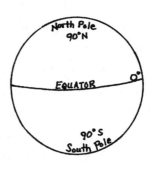

This activity helps make the concept of latitude and longitude more concrete. The supplies needed are grapefruits (one for each student) and permanent magic markers (Sharpie's recommended). Start by giving each student a grapefruit. Explain that their grapefruit represents the earth. Have each student decide where the north and south poles would be on the grapefruit. Label each pole. The North Pole represents 90 degrees north latitude, while the South Pole represents 90 degrees south latitude. Next draw a horizontal line all the way around the middle of the grapefruit so that it makes a complete circle. Have each student label this line the equator. The equator sits at zero degrees latitude.

The next step is to draw five parallel circles between the equator and the North Pole. These represent latitude lines which measure distances north of the equator. Each line represents a 15 degree interval. Label the first line above the equator 15 degrees north, the second line 30 degrees north, etc.

Finally, have the students draw five parallel circles which start just below the equator and end at the South Pole. These latitude lines are used to measure distances south of the equator. The lines are again labeled in fifteen degree intervals, with the number of degrees increasing as they approach the South Pole. The finished product will look like the illustration at left.

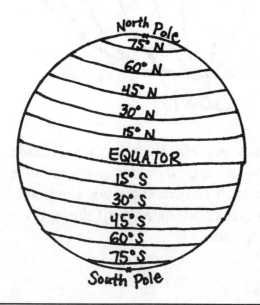

To make longitude lines, the students first draw a circle which runs perpendicular to the latitude lines and intersects both poles. This line represents zero degrees longitude. On a map or globe this line runs roughly through the center of London, England. Next have the students draw twelve equally spaced lines which each encircle the grapefruit and intersect both poles.

Hands-On Activity, page 2

The lines which spread out to the right of the zero degree longitude line measure the distance east of the equator in fifteen degree intervals. The lines which spread out to the left measure the distance to the west. The lines meet on the opposite side of the "globe" at 180 degrees. Sailors who reached this point could have entered it as 180 degrees east **or** west of London.

Accurately drawing longitude lines can be a challenging task, particularly for younger students. You may want to modify the activity to include fewer lines spreading out at wider degree intervals. Another suggestion is to use separate grapefruits for latitude and longitude. You may also want to make larger models using balls or other sizable round objects.

You can teach your students how to use latitudinal and longitudinal lines by providing coordinates which lead them to specific points on their

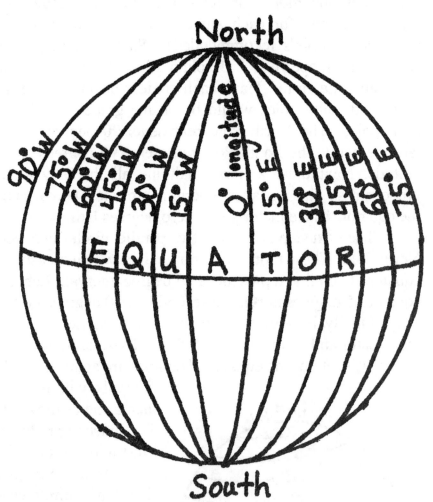

mini-globes. For example, if the coordinates given are 30 degrees north latitude, 45 degrees west longitude, the student needs to find where the 30 degree north latitude line intersects the 45 degree west longitude line. Have each student show you the point they discovered to check for understanding. Give several coordinates until the entire class learns how to use this time honored method of navigation!

Name: _____ Date: _____

Practice Plotting Points on a Map Using Latitude and Longitude Coordinates

Directions: Use the grid below to practice plotting points on a map. For each coordinate given, put a dot where you think the ship would be. In some cases, you will need to estimate where the point would be located.

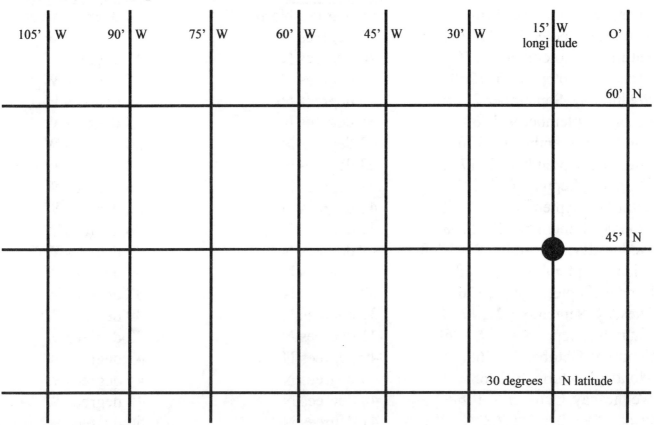

When you are finished plotting the points, connect the dots from right to left. This would have been your ship's course had you followed these coordinates!

EXAMPLE: 45' N, 15' W   This example has been plotted for you.

1. 45' N, 30' W
2. 60' N, 45' W
3. 60' N, 60' W
4. 60' N, 65' W
5. 55' N, 68' W

6. 50' N, 75' W
7. 45' N, 80' W
8. 43' N, 88' W
9. 45' N, 84' W
10. 60' N, 90' W

11. 65' N, 95' W
12. 55' N, 97' W
13. 45' N, 100' W
14. 40' N, 102' W
15. 45' N, 105' W

Navigating the Open Seas

Chart Sultana's Actual Course on a Map of the Ocean

Directions: Use the latitude and longitude readings from Sultana's captain's logs to plot the course of the ship as it sailed from England to Royal Navy headquarters in Halifax, Nova Scotia in the fall of 1768.   Use each date's latitude and longitude coordinates to record a specific point on the map provided. Connect the dots between the points to get a visual picture of the path Sultana sailed to North America!

DATE	LATITUDE	LONGITUDE
Tuesday, August 30, 1768	48 degrees North	4 degrees West
Thursday, September 1, 1768	47 degrees N	7 degrees W
Saturday, September 3, 1768	46 degrees N	11 degrees W
Monday, September 5, 1768	44 degrees N	14 degrees W
Wednesday, September 7, 1768	45 degrees N	16 degrees W
Friday, September 9, 1768	45 degrees N	18 degrees W
Sunday, September 11, 1768	43 degrees N	20 degrees W
Tuesday, September 13, 1768	43 degrees N	23 degrees W
Thursday, September 15, 1768	42 degrees N	24 degrees W
Saturday, September 17, 1768	42 degrees N	26 degrees W
Monday, September 19, 1768	41 degrees N	28 degrees W
Wednesday, September 21, 1768	41 degrees N	33 degrees W
Friday, September 23, 1768	41 degrees N	36 degrees W
Sunday, September 25, 1768	40 degrees N	37 degrees W
Tuesday, September 27, 1768	39 degrees N	39 degrees W
Thursday, September 29, 1768	41 degrees N	42 degrees W
Saturday, October 1, 1768	40 degrees N	43 degrees W
Monday, October 3, 1768	40 degrees N	44 degrees W
Wednesday, October 5, 1768	40 degrees N	48 degrees W
Friday, October 7, 1768	41 degrees N	50 degrees W
Sunday, October 9, 1768	41 degrees N	51 degrees W
Tuesday, October 11, 1768	41 degrees N	52 degrees W
Thursday, October 13, 1768	41 degrees N	55 degrees W
Saturday, October 15, 1768	41 degrees N	58 degrees W
Monday, October 17, 1768	40 degrees N	61 degrees W
Wednesday, October 19, 1768	42 degrees N	62 degrees W
Friday, October 21, 1768	43 degrees N	63 degrees W

MOORED IN HALIFAX HARBOR!

Navigating the Open Seas

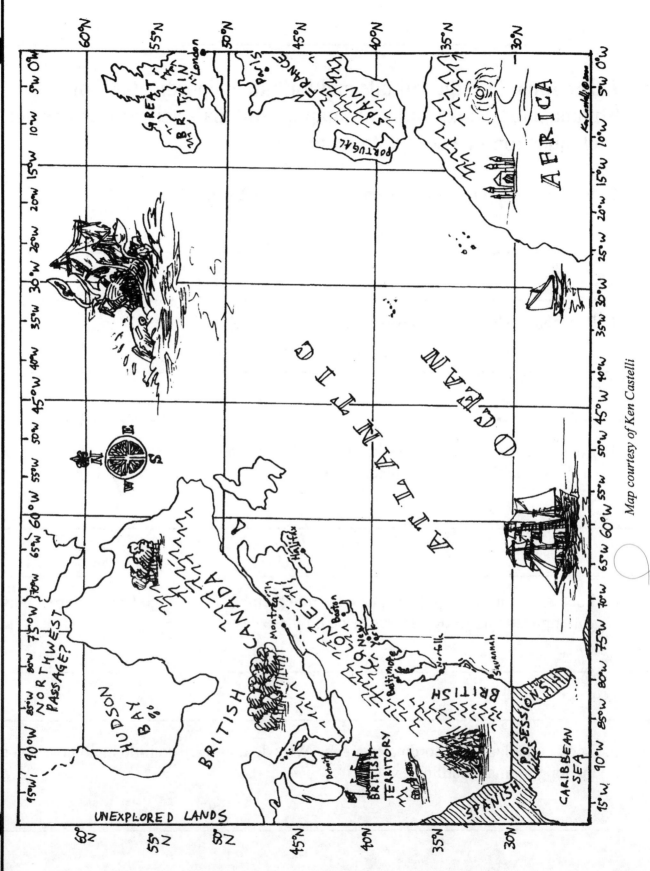

Map courtesy of Ken Castelli

Navigating the Open Seas:
Comprehension Questions

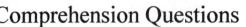

Name:_____ Date:_____

Directions: Use the latitude and longitude coordinates from Sultana's log books and your map of Sultana's sail path to answer each question in a complete sentence.

1. How long did it take for Sultana to reach North America?

_____

_____

2. In general, what direction was Sultana traveling?

_____

_____

3. Look at the progress Sultana made between September 19 and September 21, 1768. Why do you think the ship made more progress than usual on these dates?

_____

_____

4. Look at the progress Sultana made from September 29 through October 3rd. Why do you think so little progress was made on these days?

_____

_____

5. Look at the latitude coordinates given. Why do they vary so little in comparison to the longitudinal coordinates?

_____

_____

Determining Depth and Speed

When using lead lines in deep ocean water, crew members had to make sure they got plenty of line out so the weight could make it to the bottom.

Knowing the depth of the water was extremely important for captains of all ships. If the water was too shallow, the boat would run aground and possibly sink. Sometimes knowing the depth of the water helped navigators determine where they were.

Depth was measured using a tool called a lead line. This was simply a hemp rope with a heavy piece of lead tied to one end. A mark was made on the rope every six feet, which is equal to one fathom. A crew member would throw the lead line overboard, counting the marks on the line as it sank to the bottom. By multiplying the number of marks by six, the sailor could figure out how deep the water was at that spot. If a sailor counted eleven marks, for example, that meant that the depth of the water equaled sixty six feet (11 x 6 = 66 feet).

Lead lines also had another function. At the bottom of the weight was a hollow groove that the navigator filled with wax. When the weight hit the bottom, the wax collected sand, mud, or other contents of the ocean floor. If a captain knew the depth of the water and the nature of the bottom, he could make an educated guess as to where the ship was by comparing his findings to readings listed in the Nautical Almanac.

Navigators used a tool called a log line to determine the ship's speed. Log lines were made up of a wooden roller, a long length of rope, and a wooden triangle which was attached to the end of the line (see illustration below). There were knots tied into the rope every fifty feet, eight inches. The triangle, or "log", would be thrown behind the boat. As the ship moved forward, line came off the roller. Crew members kept track of how many knots went overboard in thirty seconds. The number of knots counted represented the speed of the ship in knots, or nautical miles, per hour. By knowing his ship's average speed over the course of a day, the captain could determine how far the ship had traveled.

Sultana's crew members used these methods daily to measure depth and speed. Their calculations were vital for determining the location of the ship.

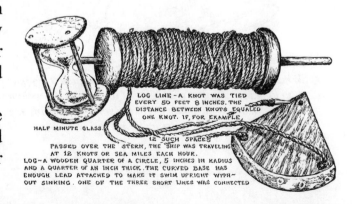

LOG LINE - A KNOT WAS TIED EVERY 50 FEET 8 INCHES. THE DISTANCE BETWEEN KNOTS EQUALED ONE KNOT. IF, FOR EXAMPLE,

HALF MINUTE GLASS

12 SUCH SPACES PASSED OVER THE STERN, THE SHIP WAS TRAVELING AT 12 KNOTS OR SEA MILES EACH HOUR. LOG - A WOODEN QUARTER OF A CIRCLE, 5 INCHES IN RADIUS AND A QUARTER OF AN INCH THICK. THE CURVED BASE HAS ENOUGH LEAD ATTACHED TO MAKE IT SWIM UPRIGHT WITH~ OUT SINKING. ONE OF THE THREE SHORT LINES WAS CONNECTED

Hands-On Activity

Make Your Own Lead Line!

Have your students measure the height of various objects in the classroom using a lead line. You will need string or twine, a weight (lead weights, fishing weights, or any other weight that can be tied to a piece of string), and a magic marker. First tie one end of the line to a weight. Next have your students make marks on the rope every fathom, or six feet. Once the line is constructed make a list of items for them to measure. This is a great activity for developing mental math skills, as many of the objects will fall between fathom marks. The students need to use their best judgment to estimate the object's length. Use the Student Task sheet provided to guide the students through the task.

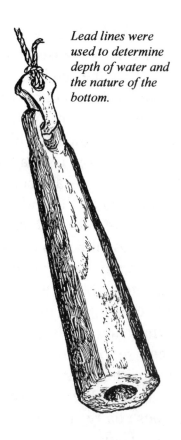

Lead lines were used to determine depth of water and the nature of the bottom.

When using lead lines in deep ocean water, crew members had to make sure they got plenty of line out so the weight could make it to the bottom. Here a sailor is twirling the weight to generate momentum for his throw.

Images reprinted from <u>Pirates and Patriots of the Revolution</u> *©2000 by C. Keith Wilbur with permission from The Globe Pequot Press, Guilford, CT, 1-800-962-0973, www.globe-pequot.com.*

Student Task: Measuring Distance with Lead

INTRODUCTION

Eighteenth century sailors used lead lines to measure the depth of the water when they were at sea. The lead line was a simple device that was made up of a long length of rope tied to a lead weight at one end. The line was marked every fathom, or six feet. One sailor would throw the weighted end of the line overboard while the other counted the marks as it went out. Once the weight hit the bottom of the sea, the depth was calculated and recorded in the ship's log in fathoms.

Today you will be making your own lead line and using it to measure the lengths of various objects in your class. In so doing, you will be using the same technology used by the sailors of Sultana over two hundred thirty years ago!

MAKING THE LEAD LINE (Groups of two to four students)

To make a lead line, your group will need the following materials from the Materials Center prepared by your teacher:
- One long length of rope or twine
- One weight (it could be lead, metal, a fishing weight, etc.)
- One magic marker

Follow these directions to make your lead line:
1. Tie your weight to one end of the line
2. Mark off the rope every fathom, or six feet, using the magic marker

Now use the lead line to measure the following items in your classroom. You will need to convert your finding into feet, fathoms, and yards (one yard = three feet).

	FEET	FATHOMS	YARDS
The height of your desk			
Your own height			
The height of the classroom door			
The length of one side of your classroom			
The height of the ceiling			

Sultana and the Chesapeake Bay

The Chesapeake Bay seen by Sultana's crew members in 1769 was a much different environment from the Bay we see today. The water was so clear that the bottom was visible in up to 30 feet of water. Submerged grass beds covered hundreds of thousands of acres of the Bay bottom and provided ideal habitat for young crabs and fish.

Oysters were once plentiful in the Chesapeake Bay.

Oysters were so plentiful that they created huge mounds which stuck out above the water at low tide and posed a navigational hazard for sailors. Giant rockfish, some weighing as much as 60 pounds, migrated up the Bay by the thousands each spring to spawn. Spring time also brought great runs of shad and herring to tidal streams during their mating season. In the Fall, millions of waterfowl flocked to the Bay during their seasonal migrations to feed on the abundance of rooted underwater plants found in shallow areas. This amazingly productive environment provided colonists with an abundant source of food.

As more settlers arrived on the Chesapeake Bay in the 1700's, the nature of the land surrounding it began to change dramatically. Huge sections of forest were cleared to make room for tobacco, corn, and grain fields. More land was cleared to make room for houses. In the latter half of the 18th century, thousands of trees were harvested to be used for ship building. These man made changes to the environment marked the beginning of the Chesapeake Bay's demise as a perfectly balanced ecosystem. When it rained on the unprotected soil found in deforested areas, sediments washed off the land and into the Bay. The loose soil clouded the water, in some cases preventing sunlight from reaching the bottom and suffocating submerged grass beds. In today's Chesapeake, visibility is generally less than five or six feet.

Huge rockfish migrated up the Bay to spawn each Spring. In the 1600's, John Smith remarked that the fish were so abundant that it appeared that a man could walk across their backs.

adult

juvenile (3")

Today people are much more aware of how their actions on land affect the health of the Chesapeake Bay. Perhaps one day the Bay will again look like it did when Sultana's crew members sailed her waters in 1769.

Illustrations courtesy of Alice Jane Lippson, selected from Life in the Chesapeake Bay, Second Edition.

Sultana and the Chesapeake Bay

NAME: _____ DATE: _____

1. In the space below, draw a picture of what the Chesapeake Bay may have looked like in 1769. Label any plants or animals you include in your illustration.

2. What changes occurred to the land surrounding the Bay in the 1700's? How did these changes on land affect the Bay?

_____

_____

_____

_____

_____

Portrait of an enslaved sailor from Rhode Island during the Revolutionary Period.

One of the crew members listed in Sultana's muster book is Prince Gould. At age 45, he was the oldest man on Sultana's crew list. He was also the only crew member in the captain's log identified as an African American. Although we don't have first hand knowledge of what his life was like on board, we can get a general picture of what he may have experienced by examining what life was like for black sailors, both free and enslaved, during this time in our history.

During the colonial period, life was difficult for African Americans. The vast majority of blacks in America in the late 1700's worked as slaves on large farms called plantations. Their days were filled with endless hours of back breaking work. Most slaves had been kidnapped from Africa, forced onto overcrowded ships, sailed across the Atlantic to the colonies, and sold to farmers along the Atlantic coast. Without the help of slave labor, plantation owners would have quickly gone out of business.

Some slaves on plantations worked as sailors. They were put in charge of small brigs and schooners to deliver crops to coastal markets for their masters. In the Chesapeake Bay, many of the smaller vessels coming in and out of major ports like Annapolis, Baltimore, and Chestertown were commanded by black captains and crews. These men spent much of their time away from their slave owners and played the important role of informing other slaves of news from distant ports.

Some African Americans in the 1760's were freedmen. In many cases the only jobs these individuals could find were on merchant or naval ships. Although life at sea was extremely demanding and dangerous, ships were one of the only places where skilled blacks could be judged based on their abilities rather than the color of their skin. Skilled black sailors were occasionally paid more and ranked higher than unskilled white sailors. Life on large ships often demanded that the crew work together despite differences in race. Jobs such as raising the anchor, raising and lowering sails, and furling topsails in heavy seas demanded cooperation amongst sailors of both races.

Enslaved blacks often assisted their masters with transporting goods to market. They sometimes sailed on sloops and schooners manned entirely by African slaves.

Blacks often acted as servants on colonial ships.

Seamen also shared living conditions which gave them a common identity. Black and white sailors wore the same clothing and spoke the same shipboard language. They shared extremely cramped living quarters, which often brought the men closer together.

While life at sea provided modest opportunities for many slaves and free blacks, there were still instances where racism led to poor treatment of these men from their white counterparts. Black sailors were often teased and ridiculed by white crew members. They often drew more than their share of beatings and punishment from harsh captains. Freed blacks at sea lived in constant fear of being captured by white slave traders and forced to work on plantations.

Racial barriers also prevented skilled black sailors from becoming officers on naval ships. Many slaves and freedmen filled servant roles such as cook, cabin boy, or ship's musician while at sea. Captains often refused to pay these men when their tour of duty expired.

How was Prince Gould treated on Sultana? There is no way of knowing for sure. What is known from the schooner's log books is that he was born in Rhode Island and joined Sultana's crew voluntarily on April 1, 1769. His brief tenure on the schooner ended on November 22, 1769 when he was discharged in Virginia because he had a hernia. Gould's old age and poor health make it unlikely that he worked on deck. Perhaps he served as the ship's cook.

Prince Gould was one of thousands of free and enslaved blacks who served as sailors during the colonial period. These men made an important contribution to our maritime history.

Africans were often captured on land, forced onto crowded slave ships, and sailed across the Atlantic Ocean to the colonies. There they were purchased by plantation owners who relied on slave labor to plant and harvest their crops. Here a group of slaves is being rowed out to a ship for transport to North America.

Images courtesy of the National Maritime Museum in London, England.

African American Experience: Compare and Contrast

NAME:_____ **DATE:**_____

Directions: Based on what you read about Prince Gould, compare and contrast the lives of black and white sailors in the 18th century. In the left hand column, list experiences that were unique to African American sailors. In the right hand column, list experiences that were unique to white sailors. In the middle column, list experiences sailors of both races had in common.

EXPERIENCES UNIQUE TO AFRICAN AMERICAN SAILORS	EXPERIENCES SHARED BY SAILORS OF BOTH RACES	EXPERIENCES UNIQUE TO WHITE SAILORS

NAME:_____ DATE:_____

STUDENT ACTIVITY #1
Use your compare and contrast chart to write a journal entry in which you compare the lives of African American and white sailors on 18th century ships. Be sure to include ways the sailors' lives were similar **and** different.

_____

_____

_____

_____

_____

_____

_____

_____

_____

_____

_____

_____

_____

_____

_____

STUDENT ACTIVITY #2
Pretend you are Prince Gould. As a 45 year old free black man in 1769, your employment options in America are extremely limited. In the space below, write a journal entry in which you explain why you have chosen to work on the Schooner Sultana.

_____

_____

_____

_____

_____

_____

_____

_____

STUDENT ACTIVITY #3
As an African American sailor in the 18th century, what are some of your concerns about working on Sultana?

_____

_____

_____

_____

_____

_____

Sails of Sultana

Colonial ships were powered by wind. Wind power was captured by the ship's sails. The more sails the captain could raise, the more power that ship had. Therefore, eighteenth century sailors used as many sails as they could possibly hoist into the sky.

Sultana had fifteen sails in all. These sails included, among others, a fore sail, main sail, fore course, two square topsails, and two jibs. The fore and main sails were the two largest sails and supplied the majority of power. The fore course was attached to the fore mast and provided additional power. The inner and outer jibs were located at the bow of the schooner and were especially useful in light wind conditions. Square topsails were attached to topmasts and were also helpful when winds were light.

Sails are held up by masts, or spars. The two largest masts on Sultana were the fore mast and main mast. Each of these masts had smaller topmasts attached to them. These masts could be moved up and down and were often removed during violent storms. Some spars lay horizontally. These spars are called yards. The upper edges of sails are attached to the yards. Yards could be raised and lowered to change the position of sails.

Several large cables on Sultana helped to hold the masts in place. The cables which run from the masts to the front and back of the ship are called stays. The cables which look like ladders and are attached to the sides of the ship are called shrouds. These are not shown in the illustration.

Colonial ships were still at nature's mercy when it came to controlling the wind itself. Boats often had to sit at anchor for days waiting for the wind to pick up or blow in the right direction. It wasn't until the invention of the steam engine that sailors weren't always dependent on wind.

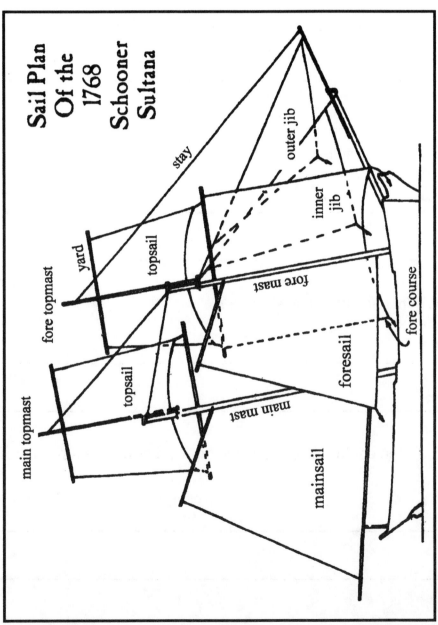

Sail Plan Of the 1768 Schooner Sultana

Sails of Sultana: Comprehension Questions

NAME: _____ **DATE:** _____

DIRECTIONS: Answer each question in a complete sentence.

1. Why did sailors use as many sails as possible?

_____

_____

2. What two sails gave Sultana most of its power?

_____

_____

3. What are spars?

_____

_____

4. What are stays and shrouds?

_____

_____

5. When could sailors' reliance on wind power be a problem?

_____

_____

_____

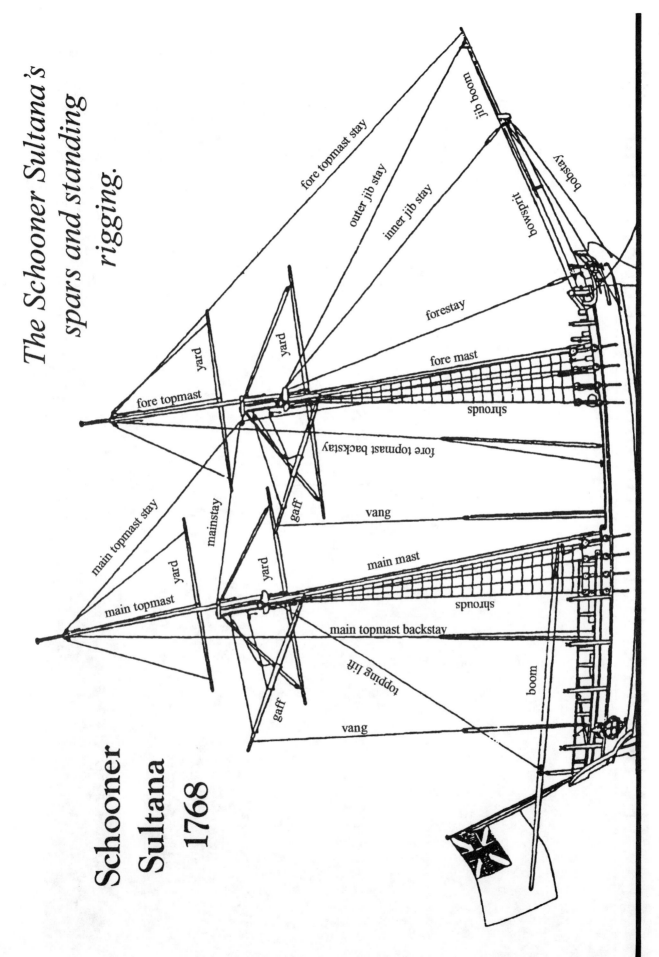

The Schooner Sultana's spars and standing rigging.

Schooner Sultana 1768

jib boom

bobstay

bowsprit

fore topmast stay

outer jib stay

inner jib stay

forestay

fore mast

yard

yard

fore topmast

shrouds

fore topmast backstay

main topmast stay

mainstay

vang

gaff

main topmast

yard

yard

main mast

main topmast

shrouds

main topmast backstay

topping lift

gaff

boom

vang

Rendering of Sultana by Mr. John Poicus

The Schooner Sultana Sailing into Philadelphia

Sultana was a frequent visitor to Philadelphia, spending time there in July 1769, April of 1770, August of 1771, and the winter of 1771-1772.
Engraving courtesy of Conway Maritime Press, London, England.

CAPTAIN'S LOG - After visiting Sultana, have each student create his/her own captain's log. In the log, have each student keep track of Sultana's daily activities during one week (or more) of operation. For each entry, the student must provide the ship's latitudinal and longitudinal coordinates, the existing weather conditions, the date of the entry, and a description of the day's events. For an added effect, stain the paper with moistened tea bags and burn the edges to create a weathered appearance. At the end of the project, have each student read his/her log entries to the class.

ART PROJECT - CREATE A SULTANA DIORAMA - Using shoe boxes, popsicle sticks, hot glue, and any other materials selected by the teacher, create a diorama of a colonial town next to the water with the 1768 Schooner Sultana anchored in the harbor. Before creating the diorama, discuss what types of buildings would have existed in an 18th century town. Once completed, have the students discuss how the colonists would have felt about Sultana's presence in their harbor.

FOLLOW-UP QUESTIONS - Have the students discuss any or all of the following questions once they return from their sailing experience with Sultana:

- How come boats like Sultana are no longer built?
- How did the sailors use simple machines? How were 18th century machines different from the machines of today?
- What do you think would have been the hardest part of living on a schooner in the 18th century? What would have been some of the enjoyable aspects of life at sea?
- What modern modes of transportation have taken the place of the wooden sailing fleet?
- How did Royal Navy vessels like Sultana help lead to the start of the American Revolution?
- How did sailors preserve their foods without refrigeration?
- How were medical practices in the 18th century different from the medical practices of today? What modern inventions do doctors have today that provide them with information that would have been inaccessible to 18th century doctors?

- Name items on the modern Sultana that would not have been present on the original ship. Discuss why those items did not exist on the original vessel.
- How did the Chesapeake Bay and its many tributaries connect the colonists of Maryland and Virginia to the international economy?
- What were some differences between Sultana's armaments and the armaments on modern warships?

Additional Resources for Teachers and Students

Books for Teachers

The Wooden World by N.A.M. Rodgers

This book provides a comprehensive view of life in the British Royal Navy. Topics discussed include the Royal Navy's politics, rules and regulations, and system of rank. Several chapters give the reader a detailed glimpse of what life may have been like aboard a Royal Navy vessel, vividly describing the ship's occupations, food rations, unique culture, and discipline. This book is available through the Sultana Ship Store at www.schoonersultana.com

The Royal Navy in America, 1760-1775 by Neil R. Stout

This book provides an excellent historical account of the years preceding the American Revolution, describing the heated political climate created by Parliament's taxes and the Royal Navy's role in exacerbating the colonists' ire towards their mother country. *Sultana* is briefly mentioned in the text.

Black Jacks by W. Jeffrey Bolster

This fascinating publication enlightens the reader with a comprehensive account of the role African American sailors played in the shipping industry during the "Age of Sail". Many of Bolster's accounts take place on the waters of the Chesapeake Bay, creating a local interest for individuals living near her waters. Bolster effectively describes the extreme hardships faced by African Americans at sea while pointing out that the seafaring life often represented the black man's best opportunity for employment and advancement.

The Patrick O'Brien Series (historical fiction)

These popular novels provide readers with factually-based accounts of warfare and shipboard life in the late 18th and early 19th centuries. The books are notorious for their historical accuracy, well developed story lines, and meticulously detailed descriptions of life at sea.

Between the Devil and the Deep Blue Sea by Marcus Rediker

This book examines the lives of merchant seamen and pirates in the first half of the 18th century. It includes descriptions of trade routes of the time, the curious waterfront societies of major port towns, and vivid accounts of the harsh working conditions and strict discipline found on 18th century vessels.

Books for Kids

Pirates and Patriots of the Revolution by C. Keith Wilbur, M.D.

A detailed account of virtually every aspect of sailing during the colonial period, this book contains a wonderful collection of illustrations depicting boat building, traditional tools and clothing, weapons, navigational instruments, sails, rigging, rations, etc. Each illustration is accompanied by text which explains that particular item. This publication is appropriate for students ages 10 to adulthood.

NOTE: All of the books listed above can be ordered through the Sultana Ship Store at www.schoonersultana.com